Y0-BDG-043

THE CAT
WHO CAME TO STAY

Lesley Fotherby

DISCARD

LONGMEADOW
P R E S S

Last spring, a white cat became a regular visitor to our garden. She would climb over the wall sometime after breakfast, settle herself in an empty flowerpot, and sleep the day away. In the evening she would be gone, though whether to return to a comfortable home or to spend an active night hunting for food, we never knew.

She seemed to walk alone, but one day, to our surprise, she was accompanied by a younger cat. The new visitor looked well-fed, with bright eyes and a charming way of looking about her as though she was at a party to which she was not sure she had been invited. This turned out to be the white cat's last visit to our garden. It was as though the black-and-white cat was her parting gift to us.

We already had two cats, but there could be no doubt – we now had a third. We called her Dancer after watching her pirouette gracefully in her white socks, chasing her tail. Her dance said, 'This is me and this is my world'.

We made her a home in the potting shed. The house was out of the question with our two jealous Burmese there. She was quite happy on some old sacking watching the spiders weave their webs over the window. Once in a while she would sweep away all their hard work with an imperious wave of a white-gloved paw.

ANDALUSIA TOWNSHIP LIBRARY

As spring turned to summer, the garden blossomed. Dancer would stalk imaginary prey through a jungle, green and dark below, brilliant with color above. The scent from the flowers made her head spin. Following her own secret paths she would momentarily lose herself. Then, leaping on a beetle, she would bring crashing down some long-stemmed tulip or angry snapdragon.

Occasionally Max, a cat of about her own age, would be invited to help explore her kingdom. Dancer enjoyed showing off in front of Max, making it clear that this was *her* territory.

It seemed as though the summer would last forever. Dancer grew bigger and stronger as the days went by. She appeared to enjoy certain exercises, flexing her muscles and improving her hunting technique. Time after time she jumped over a flowerpot twice her size, as though she was trying to prove something.

She would lurk behind a screen of plants like a tiger before reaching for a butterfly at rest on a petal. Invariably, it would flutter off safely, much to her annoyance. Once, I thought she had been stung by a wasp she swiped with her paw. She squealed and limped for a few paces before seeming to forget all about it.

Good as she now was at stalking and jumping, Dancer was defeated by the bird-table. She would make wild leaps at the birds calmly eating in safety above her. She even tried to climb the pole on which the table was fixed, but seldom got further than halfway before slipping back with comic indignation on her face. Her greatest achievement was to reach the peanut bag only to find that it tasted disgusting.

Only the most timid birds flew off the table when Dancer attacked. The cheeky robin did not even look up from his pecking, and the collared dove just stared down at her. It was all most frustrating to a cat who regarded anything with wings as her natural prey.

As Dancer felt herself more at home in the garden she would venture onto the windowsill. Perdi and Solomon, my two Burmese, would take grave offence, spitting their cat-fury at the interloper through the glass. Dancer did not blink, staring into the world so close to hers but so different.

Perdi and Solomon would chase each other round the breakfast table and up the curtains until I came to scold them. Exiled to my flower room, I would allow Dancer to pay me a brief visit before returning her to the garden.

Another cat came to call on Dancer – a large
ginger tom with yellow eyes. Dancer would come
very close to him as he pretended to be asleep.
As soon as she put out a paw and touched the
ginger fur he would get up purposefully and Dancer
would shy away. She was still rather nervous of
other cats.

As the days went by, Dancer became braver.
She made it clear she wanted to be let into
the house. I was still worried that there
would be all-out war between her and
the Burmese who were very boisterous.

One day, while we were out shopping, taking Perdi and Solomon with us as they loved going out in the car, Dancer slipped through a half-open window into my garden room off the kitchen. I kept my flowers there, after I had cut them, in buckets ready to be arranged in vases later. Perhaps this was why she felt so at home there. It was so like the garden.

She leaped from shelf to shelf, turning over cans and carpeting the floor in sodden flowers. There were still a few apples from the previous autumn, and these she rolled over the edge of the table to join the magnificent chaos below.

Dancer was now a splendid jumper.
She had no difficulty in reaching the
highest shelves. I had left a saucer of
milk that Perdi had been drinking from
on the top of a wooden crate, and this
she found most refreshing. When she
was finished in the garden room, she
ventured into the kitchen. When she
had explored the whole house
downstairs, she went up the stairs
to the bedroom.

There was so much to play with
here. The wardrobe was open and
there were dresses hanging up
just asking to be climbed. It was
a pity about the dressing-table
having so many jars and tubes
on it. Or at least they were
not on it by the time
Dancer had finished.

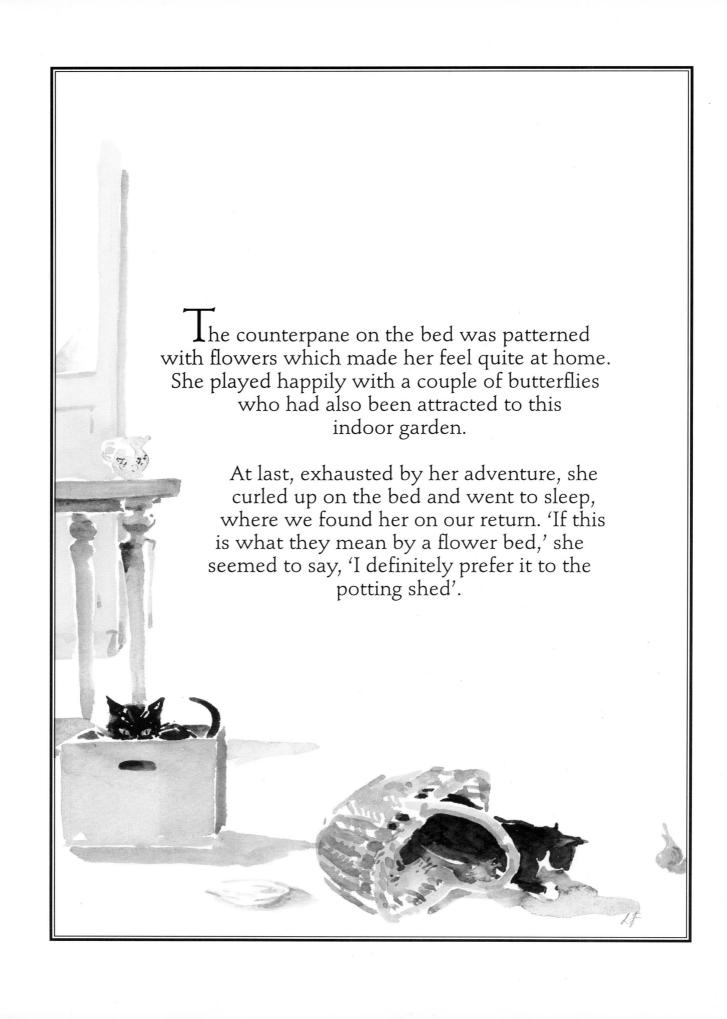

The counterpane on the bed was patterned
with flowers which made her feel quite at home.
She played happily with a couple of butterflies
who had also been attracted to this
indoor garden.

At last, exhausted by her adventure, she
curled up on the bed and went to sleep,
where we found her on our return. 'If this
is what they mean by a flower bed,' she
seemed to say, 'I definitely prefer it to the
potting shed'.

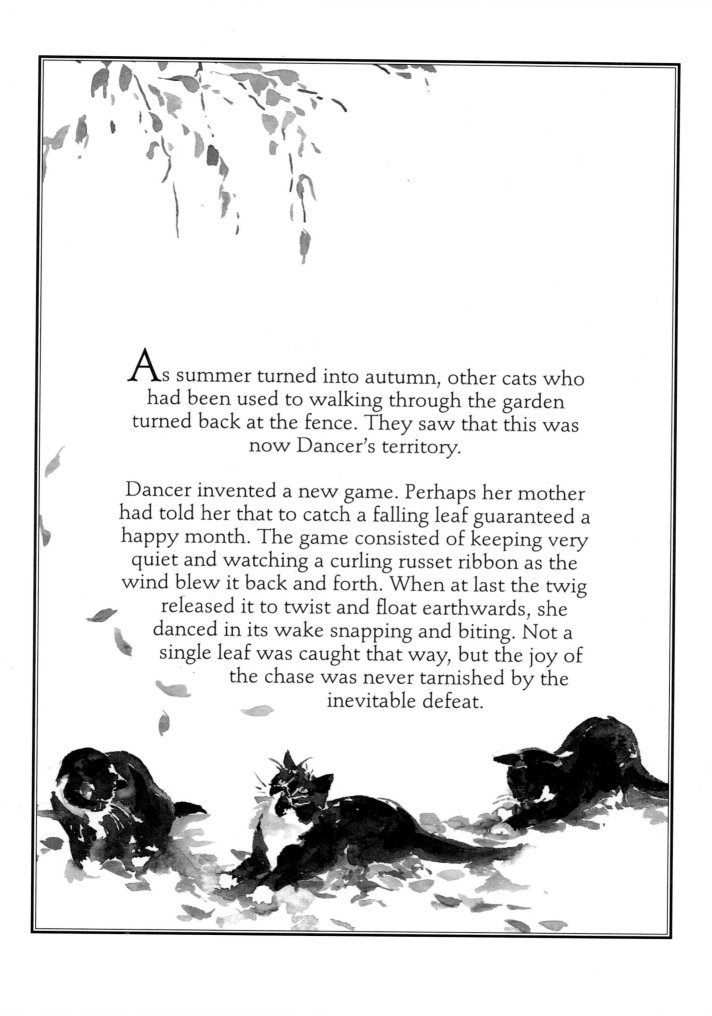

As summer turned into autumn, other cats who had been used to walking through the garden turned back at the fence. They saw that this was now Dancer's territory.

Dancer invented a new game. Perhaps her mother had told her that to catch a falling leaf guaranteed a happy month. The game consisted of keeping very quiet and watching a curling russet ribbon as the wind blew it back and forth. When at last the twig released it to twist and float earthwards, she danced in its wake snapping and biting. Not a single leaf was caught that way, but the joy of the chase was never tarnished by the inevitable defeat.

Then came the days when the leaves came down
too fast to count in clouds of red, brown and gold.
Dancer spent more and more time asleep in the
potting shed.

Had she slept for a day or a week?
As she reluctantly stretched and felt her hunger
she was almost dazzled by a bright white light.
It had snowed. Cautiously, she explored this
new element, skating, slithering and sinking
up to her nose in it. Her familiar garden had
become a foreign country.

In the evening, she came scratching at the
back door begging to be let in. She looked wet and
dejected when she went back to the potting shed,
but when I went out for a short time later I was
relieved to see her and Perdi curled up together
on some sacking. Perdi was washing her
very thoroughly.

I beckoned them into the kitchen and gave Dancer
some warm milk while Solomon looked on.
Dancer had been accepted into the family.

Soon, Dancer was playing all
Perdi's and Solomon's games. It was as
though the house had always been her empire,
never the garden which now lay under a blanket
of thick snow.

The three cats would hunt each other, leaping out
from behind pieces of furniture, pretending to be
very fierce with each other. Dancer was rather wild
at first for the comfort of the human beings who
had to share the house with her.

Dancer would frequently lead Perdi and Solomon into trouble. When all three of them tried to climb up the curtain, their combined weight brought curtain and curtain-pole crashing down on them. I was very angry and I believe Dancer knew she had gone too far.

Now she is quiet when I want her to be, and has learned that the inside of the house is not her personal adventure playground. I never knew where Dancer came from, but she sits beneath my feet as I write this, a white paw delicately stroking her nose, very much at home.

Published in the United States by
Longmeadow Press, 210 High Ridge Road, Stamford, CT 06904
First published in Great Britain by Michael O'Mara Books, London

All rights reserved.
No part of this publication may be reproduced
or utilized in any form or by any means, electronic or mechanical,
including photocopying, recording or by any information storage
and retrieval system without permission in writing
from the Publisher.

Copyright © 1992 by Lesley Fotherby

ISBN 0-681-00611-0

Designed and typeset by Martin Bristow

Printed and bound in Belgium by
Proost International Book Production

First Longmeadow Press Edition 1994
0 9 8 7 6 5 4 3 2 1